Make a New Friend in Jesus

PassAlong Arch® Books help you share Jesus with friends close to y children all around the world!

When you've enjoyed this along to a friend. When you ished, mail this book to the Outreach promises to deliver where in the world to help him

G000088480

Myself

My name _____

My address _____

_____

My PassAlong Friend

My name _____

My address _____

_____

When you're ready to give your PassAlong Arch® Book to a new friend who doesn't know about Jesus, mail it to

> **Concordia Gospel Outreach**
> **3547 Indiana Avenue**
> **St. Louis, MO 63118**

PassAlong Series

Copyright © 1995 Concordia Publishing House
3558 S. Jefferson Avenue, St. Louis, MO 63118-3968
Manufactured in the United States of America

1 2 3 4 5 6 7 8 9 10   04 03 02 01 00 99 98 97 96 95

Peter
and the
Biggest Birthday

Acts 1:1–2:47 for Children

By Carol Greene
Illustrated by Michelle Dorenkamp

SAINT LOUIS

orty days sped swiftly past
Since Easter dawned so fair.
And glad disciples came and went;
Their hearts were filled with deep content.
They knew their Lord was there.

"Those were good times."

And sometimes Jesus came to them,
    During those fleet forty days.
Sometimes they'd eat, sometimes
        they'd walk
    And listen to Lord Jesus talk
    Of heaven and its ways.

"Listen closely!"

Then Jesus rose to heaven again,
But His command was clear:
"Wait in Jerusalem, My friends,
Until your heavenly Father sends
His Holy Spirit here."

And so they waited and they prayed
The rest of Eastertide.
Matthias joined their number then,
So that they would be twelve again,
Since wicked Judas died.

"Judas sold Jesus to His enemies."

On Pentecost, in someone's house,
Where they had come together,
A mighty wind began to blow.
At least, that's how it sounded, though
It could not be the weather.

No earthly wind could sound like that.
It came from heaven instead.
And straight from heaven also came,
A glowing little tongue of flame
On each disciple's head.

"Oh! Oh!"

God's Spirit filled them all that day
And great gifts did He now bring.
Their words poured out, a perfect flow,
In languages they didn't know.
It was the strangest thing.

A crowd was milling around outside.
Then in their tracks they froze.
"Those men all come from Galilee,
But each of us quite easily,
Hears in the tongue he knows!

We come from many different lands,
And many tongues we speak.
Yet when these men God's wonders tell,
We understand them very well
In Arabic and Greek.

"In Latin and Egyptian too,
And Libyan and such.
It is a miracle we hear!"
But other men began to jeer.
"Those twelve have drunk too much."

"They have not!"

Then Peter stood up, straight and tall.
The others stood up too.
"We are not drunk. It's morning still.
But listen to me, if you will.
What God said has come true.

"Oh, good. Peter will explain."

According to the prophet Joel,
God said, 'There'll come a day
When on creation I will pour
My Spirit, and their hearts will soar
With all they have to say.

" 'And then your young will prophesy,
And holy visions see;
Your old dream dreams beneath the sun.
At that time I will save each one
Who simply calls on Me.'

"Go on, Peter.
Go on."

N ow, listen," Peter said again.
"I have so much to tell
Of Jesus, whom God sent to you,
His loving will to teach and do.
He served His Father well.

"But you, God's children, took God's Son
And nailed Him to a cross.
Upon that cross Lord Jesus died.
And on that dark day, far and wide,
Creation mourned its loss.

"It was a dreadful day!"

But God brought Him to life again.
He did! Lord Jesus lives!
And as He promised He would do,
He to us all—to me, to you—
The Holy Spirit gives."

"Easter was the best day ever!"

The words that Peter spoke that day
To many hearts cut through.
"We're guilty! We have killed God's Son.
We did not know He was the one.
And now what shall we do?"

"Repent!" said Peter. "Turn around.
Turn back to God today.
Be baptized now, my friends, and live.
The Lord is kind. He will forgive.
He loves you all, I say.

"Listen to Peter. He knows."

Repent, be baptized, friends, and live.
You'll have God's Spirit too.
God's promise isn't just for some.
It's for the world He sent His Son,
For you, my friends, for you!"

Some walked away from him that day,
As Peter begged and taught.
But many heard with great delight,
And to the Lord before that night,
Three thousand souls were brought.

So they became one close-knit group,
    All those who loved the Lord.
    They met together every day
    In homes to eat and praise and pray,
    And listen to God's Word.

    They sold their goods, the things they owned;
    Gave money to the poor.
    Their hearts grew lighter with each dawn.
    God's Spirit led them on and on.
    Their faith burned strong and sure.

Their joy made others wonder then,
And though some still felt scorn,
To those who followed Jesus' way,
God added others every day.
And so the Church was born.

Two thousand years have passed since God
Sent wind and tongues of flame.
His Spirit to the Church gave birth,
And people all around the earth,
Still meet in Jesus' name.

"The church must be millions of people by now."

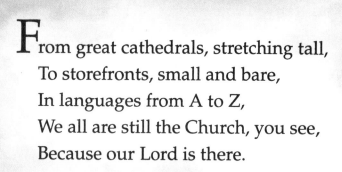

From great cathedrals, stretching tall,
To storefronts, small and bare,
In languages from A to Z,
We all are still the Church, you see,
Because our Lord is there.